In My Sky at Twilight
Poems of Eternal Love

Gaby Morgan is the Editorial Director of the Macmillan Children's Books Poetry list. She has edited a number of bestselling anthologies, including *Read Me: A Poem for Every Day of the Year*; *Christmas Poems* and *Fairy Poems*, which was shortlisted for the CLPE Poetry Award. She lives in Hampshire with Grant, Jude and Evie.

In My Sky at Twilight

Poems of Eternal Love

Chosen by Gaby Morgan

MACMILLAN

First published 2010 by Macmillan Children's Books
a division of Macmillan Publishers Limited
20 New Wharf Road, London N1 9RR
Basingstoke and Oxford
Associated companies throughout the world
www.panmacmillan.com

ISBN 978-0-230-74586-5

1 3 5 7 9 8 6 4 2

A CIP catalogue record for this book is available from
the British Library.

Typeset by Ellipsis Books Limited
Printed and bound in the UK by CPI Mackays, Chatham ME5 8TD

For Grant – We'll always have Pontefract . . .
Yours eternally, Mrs Weston

and for Robert Pattinson

Contents

In My Sky at Twilight

In my sky at twilight you are like a cloud
and your form and colour are the way I love them.
You are mine, mine, woman with sweet lips
and in your life my infinite dreams live.

The lamp of my soul dyes your feet,
the sour wine is sweeter on your lips,
oh reaper of my evening song,
how solitary dreams believe you to be mine!

You are mine, mine, I go shouting it to the afternoon's
wind, and the wind hauls on my widowed voice.
Huntress of the depths of my eyes, your plunder
stills your nocturnal regard as though it were water.

You are taken in the net of my music, my love,
and my nets of music are wide as the sky.
My soul is born on the shore of your eyes of mourning.
In your eyes of mourning the land of dreams begins.

Pablo Neruda

'O lurcher-loving collier, black as night'

O lurcher-loving collier, black as night,
Follow your love across the smokeless hill;
Your lamp is out, the cages all are still;
Course for her heart and do not miss,
For Sunday soon is past and, Kate, fly not so fast,
For Monday comes when none may kiss:
Be marble to his soot, and to his black be white.

W. H. Auden

'Bright Star! would I were steadfast as thou art'

Bright Star! would I were steadfast as thou art –
Not in lone splendour hung aloft the night,
And watching, with eternal lids apart,
Like Nature's patient sleepless Eremite,
The moving waters at their priestlike task
Of pure ablution round earth's human shores,
Or gazing on the new soft-fallen mask
Of snow upon the mountains and the moors –
No – yet still steadfast, still unchangeable,
Pillowed upon my fair love's ripening breast
To feel for ever its soft fall and swell,
Awake for ever in a sweet unrest;
   Still, still to hear her tender-taken breath,
   And so live ever – or else swoon to death.

John Keats

First Love

I ne'er was struck before that hour
    With love so sudden and so sweet
Her face it bloomed like a sweet flower
    And stole my heart away complete
My face turned pale a deadly pale
    My legs refused to walk away
And when she looked what could I ail
    My life and all seemed turned to clay

And then my blood rushed to my face
    And took my eyesight quite away
The trees and bushes round the place
    Seemed midnight at noon day
I could not see a single thing
    Words from my eyes did start
They spoke as chords do from the string
    And blood burnt round my heart

Are flowers the winters choice
  Is love's bed always snow
She seemed to hear my silent voice
  Not loves appeals to know
I never saw so sweet a face
  As that I stood before
My heart has left its dwelling place
  And can return no more –

John Clare

When I Was One-and-Twenty

When I was one-and-twenty
I heard a wise man say,
'Give crowns and pounds and guineas
But not your heart away;
Give pearls away and rubies
But keep your fancy free.'
But I was one-and-twenty,
No use to talk to me.

When I was one-and-twenty
I heard him say again,
'The heart out of the bosom
Was never given in vain;
'Tis paid with sighs a plenty
And sold for endless rue.'
And I am two-and-twenty
And oh, 'tis true, 'tis true.

A. E. Housman

Love and Sleep

Lying asleep between the strokes of night
   I saw my love lean over my sad bed,
   Pale as the duskiest lily's leaf or head,
Smooth-skinned and dark, with bare throat made to bite,
Too wan for blushing and too warm for white,
   But perfect-coloured without white or red.
   And her lips opened amorously, and said –
I wist not what, saving one word – Delight.

And all her face was honey to my mouth,
   And all her body pasture to mine eyes;
     The long lithe arms and hotter hands than fire,
The quivering flanks, hair smelling of the south,
   The bright light feet, the splendid supple thighs
   And glittering eyelids of my soul's desire.

A. C. Swinburne

Love's Philosophy

The fountains mingle with the river
And the rivers with the ocean,
The winds of heaven mix for ever
With a sweet emotion;
Nothing in the world is single,
All things by a law divine
In one another's being mingle –
Why not I with thine?

See the mountains kiss high heaven
And the waves clasp one another;
No sister-flower would be forgiven
If it disdain'd its brother:

And the sunlight clasps the earth,
And the moonbeams kiss the sea –
What are all these kissings worth,
If thou kiss not me?

Percy Bysshe Shelley

Love What It Is

Love is a circle that doth restless move
In the same sweet eternity of love.

Robert Herrick

Balade Simple

O mighty goddess, day star after night,
Gladding the morrow when ye do appear,
To void darkness thorough freshness of your sight,
Only with twinkling of your pleasant cheer,
To you we thank, lovers that been here,
That this man – and never for to twin –
Fortuned have his lady for to win.

John Lydgate

Song

I hid my love when young while I
Couldn't bear the buzzing of a flye
I hid my love to my despite
Till I could not bear to look at light
I dare not gaze upon her face
But left her memory in each place
Where e'er I saw a wild flower lye
I kissed and bade my love goodbye

I met her in the greenest dells
Where dew-drops pearl the wood bluebells
The lost breeze kissed her bright blue eye
The bee kissed and went singing bye
A sunbeam found a passage there
A gold chain round her neck so fair
As secret as the wild bee's song
She lay there all the summer long

I hid my love in field and town
Till e'en the breeze would knock me down
The bees seemed singing ballads o'er
The flye's buzz turned a lion's roar
And even silence found a tongue
To haunt me all the summer long
The riddle nature could not prove
Was nothing else but secret love

John Clare

Thee, Thee, Only Thee

The dawning of morn, the daylight's sinking,
The night's long hours still find me thinking
   Of thee, thee, only thee.
When friends are met, and goblets crown'd,
   And smiles are near that once enchanted,
Unreach'd by all that sunshine round,
   My soul, like some dark spot, is haunted
   By thee, thee, only thee.

Whatever in fame's high path could waken
My spirit once is now forsaken
   For thee, thee, only thee.
Like shores by which some headlong bark
   To the ocean hurries, resting never,
Life's scenes go by me, bright or dark
   I know not, heed not, hastening ever
   To thee, thee, only thee.

I have not a joy but of thy bringing,
And pain itself seems sweet when springing
    From thee, thee, only thee.
Like spells that nought on earth can break,
    Till lips that know the charm have spoken,
This heart, howe'er the world may wake
    Its grief, its scorn, can but be broken
    By thee, thee, only thee.

Thomas Moore

'Blest, blest and happy he'

Blest, blest and happy he
Whose eyes behold her face,
But blessed more whose ears hath heard
The speeches framed with grace.

And he is half a god
That these thy lips may kiss,
Yet god all whole that may enjoy
    Thy body as it is.

Anon.

The Passionate Shepherd to His Love

Come live with me and be my Love,
And we will all the pleasures prove
That hills and valleys, dale and field,
And all the craggy mountains yield.

There will we sit upon the rocks
And see the shepherds feed their flocks,
By shallow rivers, to whose falls
Melodious birds sing madrigals.

There will I make thee beds of roses
And a thousand fragrant posies,
A cap of flowers, and a kirtle
Embroider'd all with leaves of myrtle.

A gown made of the finest wool,
Which from our pretty lambs we pull,
Fair linèd slippers for the cold,
With buckles of the purest gold.

A belt of straw and ivy buds
With coral clasps and amber studs:
And if these pleasures may thee move,
Come live with me and be my Love.

Thy silver dishes for thy meat
As precious as the gods do eat,
Shall on an ivory table be
Prepared each day for thee and me.

The shepherd swains shall dance and sing
For thy delight each May-morning:
If these delights thy mind may move,
Then live with me and be my Love.

Christopher Marlowe

Schoolgirl on a Train

When the girl
I'd never seen before
Who wore the tie
And scarlet uniform
Of the Catholic School
And whose dark eyes
Had almost stopped
The passage of my fifteen-year-old blood
Rose to leave the train
At the station after the golf course
I prayed she'd leave behind
The magazine she read so avidly
So I could read
The selfsame words her eyes had read
And whisper to myself
She read that
She read that
She read that.

Gareth Owen

The Canonization

For God's sake hold your tongue, and let me love,
 Or chide my palsy, or my gout,
My five grey hairs, or ruined fortune flout,
 With wealth your state, your mind with arts improve,
  Take you a course, get you a place,
  Observe his Honour, or his Grace,
Or the King's real, or his stamped face
 Contemplate; what you will, approve,
 So you will let me love.

Alas, alas, who's injured by my love?
 What merchant's ships have my sighs drowned?
Who says my tears have overflowed his ground?
 When did my colds a forward spring remove?
  When did the heats which my veins fill
  Add one more to the plaguy bill?
Soldiers find wars, and lawyers find out still
 Litigious men, which quarrels move,
 Though she and I do love.

Call us what you will, we are made such by love;
 Call her one, me another fly,
We are tapers too, and at our own cost die,
 And we in us find the eagle and the dove,

The phoenix riddle hath more wit
By us; we two being one, are it.
So to one neutral thing both sexes fit
We die and rise the same, and prove
Mysterious by this love.

We can die by it, if not live by love,
And if unfit for tombs and hearse
Our legend be, it will be fit for verse;
And if no piece of chronicle we prove,
We'll build in sonnets pretty rooms;
As well a well wrought urn becomes
The greatest ashes, as half-acre tombs,
And by these hymns, all shall approve
Us canonized for love:

And thus invoke us; 'You whom reverend love
Made one another's hermitage;
You, to whom love was peace, that now is rage;
Who did the whole world's soul contract, and drove
Into the glasses of your eyes
(So made such mirrors, and such spies,
That they did all to you epitomize,)
Countries, towns, courts: beg from above
A pattern of your love!'

John Donne

To the Virgins, to Make Much of Time

Gather ye Rose-buds while ye may,
  Old Time is still a flying:
And this same flower that smiles to day,
  Tomorrow will be dying.

The glorious Lamp of Heaven, the Sun,
  The higher he's a getting;
The sooner will his Race be run,
  And nearer he's to Setting.

That Age is best, which is the first,
  When Youth and Blood are warmer;
But being spent, the worse, and worst
  Times, still succeed the former.

Then be not coy, but use your time;
  And while ye may, go marry:
For having lost but once your prime,
  You may for ever tarry.

Robert Herrick

To Celia

Drink to me only with thine eyes,
And I will pledge with mine;
Or leave a kiss but in the cup
And I'll not look for wine.
The thirst that from the soul doth rise
Doth ask a drink divine;
But might I of Jove's nectar sup,
I would not change for thine.

I sent thee late a rosy wreath,
Not so much honouring thee,
As giving it a hope that there
It could not wither'd be.
But thou thereon didst only breathe,
And sent'st it back to me;
Since when it grows, and smells, I swear,
Not of itself, but thee.

Ben Jonson

Come into the Garden Maud
from *Maud*

I

Come into the garden, Maud,
   For the black bat, night, has flown,
Come into the garden, Maud,
   I am here at the gate alone;
And the woodbine spices are wafted abroad,
   And the musk of the rose is blown.

II

For a breeze of morning moves,
   And the planet of Love is on high,
Beginning to faint in the light that she loves
   On a bed of daffodil sky,
To faint in the light of the sun she loves,
   To faint in his light, and to die.

Alfred, Lord Tennyson

Night Thoughts

Stars, you are unfortunate, I pity you,
Beautiful as you are, shining in your glory,
Who guide seafaring men through stress and peril
And have no recompense from gods or mortals,
Love you do not, nor do you know what love is.
Hours that are aeons urgently conducting
Your figures in a dance through the vast heaven,
What journey have you ended in this moment,
Since lingering in the arms of my beloved
I lost all memory of you and midnight.

Johann Wolfgang von Goethe

Ruth

She stood breast high amid the corn,
Clasped by the golden light of morn,
Like the sweetheart of the sun,
Who many a glowing kiss had won.

On her cheek an autumn flush,
Deeply ripened; – such a blush
In the midst of brown was born,
Like red poppies grown with corn.

Round her eyes her tresses fell,
Which were blackest none could tell,
But long lashes veiled a light,
That had else been all too bright.

And her hat, with shady brim,
Made her tressy forehead dim; –
Thus she stood amid the stooks.
Praising God with sweetest looks; –

Sure, I said, heaven did not mean,
Where I reap thou shouldst but glean,
Lay thy sheaf adown and come,
Share my harvest and my home.

Thomas Hood

The Drunk and the Night Runner

This bench, between the sea
and the castle, tell me,
what colour did they choose
for the serpents' hundredth coat?
I only remember sky blue.

As you run past, by moonlight
I raise my head, disturbed
by the rhythm of your feet
against the rhythm of the tide.
It is the rhythm of my heart.

I raise an arm, to wave
only to wave, my love.
And perhaps you wave too,
wave back, as you run past.

Paul Henry

An Hour with Thee

An hour with thee! When earliest day
Dapples with gold the eastern grey,
Oh, what can frame my mind to bear
The toil and turmoil, cark and care,
New griefs, which coming hours unfold,
And sad remembrance of the old?
        One hour with thee.

One hour with thee! When burning June
Waves his red flag at pitch of noon;
What shall repay the faithful swain,
His labour on the sultry plain;
And, more than cave or sheltering bough,
Cool feverish blood and throbbing brow?
        One hour with thee.

One hour with thee! When sun is set,
Oh, what can teach me to forget
The thankless labours of the day;
The hopes, the wishes, flung away;
The increasing wants, and lessening gains,
The master's pride, who scorns my pains?
        One hour with thee.

Sir Walter Scott

Cherry-Ripe

There is a garden in her face
   Where roses and white lilies blow;
A heavenly paradise is that place,
   Wherein all pleasant fruits do flow:
     There cherries grow which none may buy
     Till 'Cherry-ripe' themselves do cry.

Those cherries fairly do enclose
   Of orient pearls a double row,
Which when her lovely laughter shows,
   They look like rose-buds filled with snow;
     Yet them nor peer nor prince can buy
     Till 'Cherry-ripe' themselves do cry.

Her eyes like angels watch them still;
   Her brows like bended bows do stand,
Threatening with piercing frowns to kill
   All that attempt with eye or hand
     Those sacred cherries to come nigh,
     Till 'Cherry-ripe' themselves do cry.

Thomas Campion

Envelopes and Letters

She felt the shock of love
Was like that moment in a dream
When the whole earth opened up on emptiness
And the falling was for ever
And for ever.

And walking here and there
Down thronging corridors
Among the desks and chairs
She threaded through the other girls
Leaving her silence in the air
Like a scented wake to occupy the space.

And sitting at her desk in History
All unbeckoned, the thought came in
That she was like an envelope
That bore nor name nor destination;
And what she felt was like a letter
The boy had scrawled his name and life upon.
She thought this when the teacher
Questioned her about the dream she occupied
Saying only
Nothing, Miss, nothing,
It's nothing.

Gareth Owen

To a Stranger

Passing stranger! you do not know
How longingly I look upon you,
You must be he I was seeking,
Or she I was seeking
(It comes to me as a dream)

I have somewhere surely
Lived a life of joy with you,
All is recall'd as we flit by each other,
Fluid, affectionate, chaste, matured,

You grew up with me,
Were a boy with me or a girl with me,
I ate with you and slept with you, your body has become
not yours only nor left my body mine only,

You give me the pleasure of your eyes,
face, flesh as we pass,
You take of my beard, breast, hands,
in return,

I am not to speak to you, I am to think of you
when I sit alone or wake at night, alone
I am to wait, I do not doubt I am to meet you again
I am to see to it that I do not lose you.

Walt Whitman

Sudden Light

I have been here before,
　　But when or how I cannot tell:
I know the grass beyond the door,
　　The sweet keen smell,
The sighing sound, the lights around the shore.

You have been mine before, –
　　How long ago I may not know
But just when at that swallow's soar
　　Your neck turned so,
Some veil did fall, – I knew it all of yore.

Has this been thus before?
　　And shall not thus time's eddying flight
Still with our lives our love restore
　　In death's despite,
And day and night yield one delight once more?

Dante Gabriel Rossetti

He Fumbles at Your Spirit

He fumbles at your Spirit
As Players at the Keys
Before they drop full Music on –
He stuns you by degrees –
Prepares your brittle Nature
For the Ethereal Blow
By fainter Hammers – further heard –
Then nearer – Then so slow
Your Breath has time to straighten –
Your Brain – to bubble Cool –
Deals – One – imperial – Thunderbolt –
That scalps your naked Soul –

When Winds take Forests in their Paws
The Universe – is still –

Emily Dickinson

The Bait

Come live with me, and be my love,
And we will some new pleasures prove
Of golden sands, and crystal brooks,
With silken lines, and silver hooks.

There will the river whispering run
Warmed by thy eyes, more than the sun.
And there the'enamoured fish will stay,
Begging themselves they may betray.

When thou wilt swim in that live bath,
Each fish, which every channel hath,
Will amorously to thee swim,
Gladder to catch thee, than thou him.

If thou, to be so seen, be'st loth,
By sun, or moon, thou darkenest both,
And if myself have leave to see,
I need not their light, having thee.

Let others freeze with angling reeds,
And cut their legs, with shells and weeds,
Or treacherously poor fish beset,
With strangling snare, or windowy net:

Let coarse bold hands, from slimy nest
The bedded fish in banks out-wrest,
Or curious traitors, sleavesilk flies
Bewitch poor fishes' wandering eyes.

For thee, thou need'st no such deceit,
For thou thyself art thine own bait,
That fish, that is not catched thereby,
Alas, is wiser far than I.

John Donne

Meeting at Night

I

The grey sea and the long black land;
And the yellow half-moon large and low;
And the startled little waves that leap
In fiery ringlets from their sleep,
As I gain the cove with pushing prow,
And quench its speed i' the slushy sand.

II

Then a mile of warm sea-scented beach;
Three fields to cross till a farm appears;
A tap at the pane, the quick sharp scratch
And blue spurt of a lighted match,
And a voice less loud, through its joys and fears,
Than the two hearts beating each to each!

Robert Browning

The Licorice Fields at Pontefract

In the licorice fields at Pontefract
   My love and I did meet
And many a burdened licorice bush
   Was blooming round our feet;
Red hair she had and golden skin,
Her sulky lips were shaped for sin,
Her sturdy legs were flannel-slack'd,
The strongest legs in Pontefract.

The light and dangling licorice flowers
   Gave off the sweetest smells;
From various black Victorian towers
   The Sunday evening bells
Came pealing over dales and hills
And tanneries and silent mills
And lowly streets where country stops
And little shuttered corner shops.

She cast her blazing eyes on me
  And plucked a licorice leaf;
I was her captive slave and she
  My red-haired robber chief.
Oh love! for love I could not speak,
It left me winded, wilting, weak
And held in brown arms strong and bare
And wound with flaming ropes of hair.

John Betjeman

I Will Make You Brooches

I will make you brooches and toys for your delight
Of bird-song at morning and star-shine at night.
I will make a palace fit for you and me,
Of green days in forests and blue days at sea.

I will make my kitchen, and you shall keep your room,
Where white flows the river and bright blows the
    broom,
And you shall wash your linen and keep your body
    white
In rainfall at morning and dewfall at night.

And this shall be for music when no one else is near,
The fine song for singing, the rare song to hear!
That only I remember, that only you admire,
Of the broad road that stretches and the roadside fire.

Robert Louis Stevenson

Always

When the wind dies
And the trees grow still,
I shall be thinking of you.
When the waves leave the shores
And head for home,
I shall be thinking of you.
When the sun settles into night
And the lights come on,
I shall be thinking of you.
Thinking of you.
Of you.
Always.

Philip Ardagh

Love and Friendship

Love is like the wild rose briar,
Friendship, like the holly tree
The holly is dark when the rose briar blooms,
But which will bloom most constantly?

The wild rose briar is sweet in spring,
Its summer blossoms scent the air
Yet wait till winter comes again
And who will call the wild-briar fair?

Then scorn the silly rose-wreath now
And deck thee with the holly's sheen
That when December blights thy brow
He still may leave thy garland green –

Emily Jane Brontë

'Your fair looks enflame my desire'

Your fair looks enflame my desire:
  Quench it again with love.
Stay, O strive not still to retire,
  Do not inhuman prove.
If love may persuade,
  Loves pleasures, dear, deny not;
Hear is a silent grovie shade:
  O tarry then, and flie not.

Have I seized my heavenly delight
  In this unhaunted grove?
Time shall now her fury require
  With the revenge of love.
Then come, sweetest, come,
  My lips with kisses gracing:
Here let us harbour all alone,
  Die, die in sweet embracing.

41

Will you now so timely depart,
   And not return again?
Your sight lends such life to my heart
   That to depart is pain.
Fear yields no delay,
   Secureness helpeth pleasure:
Then, till the time gives safer stay,
   O farewell, my lives treasure!

Thomas Campion

The More Loving One

Looking up at the stars, I know quite well
That, for all they care, I can go to hell,
But on earth indifference is the least
We have to dread from man or beast.

How should we like it were stars to burn
With a passion for us we could not return?
If equal affection cannot be,
Let the more loving one be me.

Admirer as I think I am
Of stars that do not give a damn,
I cannot, now I see them, say
I missed one terribly all day.

Were all stars to disappear or die,
I should learn to look at an empty sky
And feel its total dark sublime,
Though this might take me a little time.

W. H. Auden

Meeting

Again I see my bliss at hand,
The town, the lake are here;
My Marguerite smiles upon the strand,
Unaltered with the year.

I know that graceful figure fair,
That cheek of languid hue;
I know that soft, enkerchiefed hair,
And those sweet eyes of blue.

Again I spring to make my choice;
Again in tones of ire
I hear a God's tremendous voice:
'Be counselled, and retire.'

Ye guiding Powers who join and part,
What would ye have with me?
Ah, warn some more ambitious heart,
And let the peaceful be!

Matthew Arnold

'Western wind, when wilt thou blow'

Western wind, when wilt thou blow
   The small rain down can rain?
Christ, if my love were in my arms
   And I in my bed again!

Anon.

The Avenue

Who has not seen their lover
Walking at ease,
Walking like any other
A pavement under trees,
Not singular, apart,
But footed, featured, dressed,
Approaching like the rest
In the same dapple of the summer caught;
Who has not suddenly thought
With swift surprise:
There walks in cool disguise,
There comes, my heart.

Frances Cornford

'She tells her love while half asleep'

She tells her love while half asleep,
  In the dark hours,
    With half-words whispered low:
As Earth stirs in her winter sleep
  And puts out grass and flowers
    Despite the snow,
    Despite the falling snow.

Robert Graves

Words, Wide Night

Somewhere on the other side of this wide night
and the distance between us, I am thinking of you.
The room is turning slowly away from the moon.

This is pleasurable. Or shall I cross that out and say
it is sad? In one of the tenses I singing
an impossible song of desire that you cannot hear.

La lala la. See? I close my eyes and imagine
the dark hills I would have to cross
to reach you. For I am in love with you and this

is what it is like or what it is like in words.

Carol Ann Duffy

Violin Tide

And this is the sea, of course,
scrawling by moonlight in its room,
not quite getting the line right
where it meets the shore.

The earliest hours still find me
thinking of you; somnolent tides
rise towards daylight.
Perhaps you have drowned in me.

A table lamp shines the grain
of an old violin in the grate
and down the slope from your dreams
the bay similarly shines.

Perhaps you are not so far away
from the moon in the violin
and the clock I should wind, to hear
the workings of the bay.

At least in your dreams
see how I can not get this line
to make sense of the sand,
and how I am running out of time

and how easily the night and the day
exchange places, the land and the sea.

Paul Henry

Stella's Birth-Day

Stella this day is thirty-four,
(We shan't dispute a year or more:)
However, Stella, be not troubled,
Although thy size and years are doubled
Since first I saw thee at sixteen,
The brightest virgin on the green;
So little is thy form declined;
Made up so largely in thy mind.
O, would it please the gods to split
Thy beauty, size, and years, and wit!
No age could furnish out a pair
Of nymphs so graceful, wise, and fair;
With half the lustre of your eyes,
With half your wit, your years, and size.
And then, before it grew too late,
How should I beg of gentle fate,
(That either nymph might have her swain,)
To split my worship too in twain.

Jonathan Swift

The First Day

I wish I could remember the first day,
First hour, first moment of your meeting me,
If bright or dim the season, it might be
Summer or Winter for aught I can say.
So unrecorded did it slip away,
So blind was I to see and foresee,
So dull to mark the budding of my tree
That would not blossom yet for many a May.
If only I could recollect it, such
A day of days! I let it come and go
As traceless as a thaw of bygone snow;
It seemed to mean so little, meant so much;
If only now I could recall that touch,
First touch of hand in hand – Did one but know!

Christina Rossetti

Sonnet 116

Let me not to the marriage of true minds
Admit impediments. Love is not love
Which alters when it alteration finds,
Or bends with the remover to remove:
O, no, it is an ever-fixed mark,
That looks on tempests and is never shaken;
It is the star to every wandering bark,
Whose worth's unknown, although his height be taken.
Love's not Time's fool, though rosy lips and cheeks
Within his bending sickle's compass come;
Love alters not with his brief hours and weeks,
But bears it out even to the edge of doom.
   If this be error and upon me proved,
   I never writ, nor no man ever loved.

William Shakespeare

A Birthday

My heart is like a singing bird
   Whose nest is in a watered shoot;
My heart is like an apple tree
   Whose boughs are bent with thickset fruit;
My heart is like a rainbow shell
   That paddles in a halcyon sea;
My heart is gladder than all these
   Because my love is come to me.

Raise me a dais of silk and down;
   Hang it with vair and purple dyes;
Carve it in doves and pomegranates
   And peacocks with a hundred eyes;
Work it in gold and silver grapes,
   In leaves and silver fleurs-de-lys;
Because the birthday of my life
   Is come, my love is come to me.

Christina Rossetti

Sonnet 18

Shall I compare thee to a summer's day?
Thou art more lovely and more temperate:
Rough winds do shake the darling buds of May,
And summer's lease hath all too short a date:
Sometime too hot the eye of heaven shines,
And often is his gold complexion dimm'd,
And every fair from fair sometime declines,
By chance or natures changing course untrimm'd:
But thy eternal summer shall not fade,
Nor lose possession of that fair thou owest,
Nor shall death brag thou wandrest in his shade,
When in eternal lines to time thou growest,
   So long as men can breathe or eyes can see
   So long lives this, and this gives life to thee.

William Shakespeare

Her Song

For no other reason than I love him wholly
I am here; for this one night at least
The world has shrunk to a boyish breast
On which my head, brilliant and exhausted, rests,
And can know of nothing more complete.

Let the dawn assemble all its guilts, its worries
And small doubts that, but for love, would infect
This perfect heart.
I am as far beyond doubt as the sun.
I am as far beyond doubt as is possible.

Brian Patten

Valentine

My heart has made its mind up
And I'm afraid it's you.
Whatever you've got lined up,
My heart has made its mind up
And if you can't be signed up
This year, next year will do.
My heart has made its mind up
And I'm afraid it's you.

Wendy Cope

i carry your heart with me

i carry your heart with me(i carry it in
my heart)i am never without it(anywhere
i go you go,my dear;and whatever is done
by only me is your doing,my darling)
                                    i fear
no fate(for you are my fate,my sweet)i want
no world(for beautiful you are my world,my true)
and it's you are whatever a moon has always meant
and whatever a sun will always sing is you

here is the deepest secret nobody knows
(here is the root of the root and the bud of the bud
and the sky of the sky of a tree called life;which grows
higher than soul can hope or mind can hide)
and this is the wonder that's keeping the stars apart

i carry your heart(i carry it in my heart)

                                    E. E. Cummings

The Bargain

My true love hath my heart, and I have his,
  By just exchange one for another given:
I hold his dear, and mine he cannot miss,
  There never was a better bargain driven:
    My true love hath my heart, and I have his.

His heart in me keeps him and me in one,
  My heart in him his thoughts and senses guides:
He loves my heart, for once it was his own,
  I cherish his because in me it bides:
    My true love hath my heart, and I have his.

Sir Philip Sidney

I Do Not Love You

I do not love you as if you were salt-rose, or topaz,
or the arrow of carnations the fire shoots off.
I love you as certain dark things are to be loved,
in secret, between the shadow and the soul.

I love you as the plant that never blooms
but carries in itself the light of hidden flowers;
thanks to your love a certain solid fragrance,
risen from the earth, lives darkly in my body.

I love you without knowing how, or when, or from
   where.
I love you straightforwardly, without complexities or
   pride;
so I love you because I know no other way

than this: where *I* does not exist, nor *you*,
so close that your hand on my chest is my hand,
so close that your eyes close as I fall asleep.

Pablo Neruda

'Although I conquer all the earth'

Although I conquer all the earth,
Yet for me there is only one city.
In that city there is for me only one house;
And in that house, one room only;
And in that room, a bed.
And one woman sleeps there,
The shining joy and jewel of all my kingdom.

Anon.

My Woman

My woman says she wants no other lover
    than me, not even Jupiter himself.
She says so. What a woman says to an eager
    sweetheart
        write on the wind, write on the rushing
        waves.

Catullus

Our Love Is Loud

Our love is loud
Like fireworks and cannons
Like cheering crowds
Like a thousand tin cans tied to
A million camper vans
All backfiring and jamming on their squealing
    brakes
And hitting a billion horns
As the wailing police cars
Take up the chase
And an exploding gas main sends
A mushroom cloud like an exclamation mark
Into the thundering sky

Roger Stevens

'The sun has burst the sky'

The sun has burst the sky
Because I love you
And the river its banks.

The sea laps the great rocks
Because I love you
And takes no heed of the moon dragging it away
And saying coldly 'Constancy is not for you'.

The blackbird fills the air
Because I love you
With spring and lawns and shadows falling on lawns.

The people walk in the street and laugh
I love you
And far down the river ships sound their hooters
Crazy with joy because I love you.

Jenny Joseph

Lullaby

Lay your sleeping head, my love,
Human on my faithless arm;
Time and fevers burn away
Individual beauty from
Thoughtful children, and the grave
Proves the child ephemeral:
But in my arms till break of day
Let the living creature lie,
Mortal, guilty, but to me
The entirely beautiful.

Soul and body have no bounds:
To lovers as they lie upon
Her tolerant enchanted slope
In their ordinary swoon,
Grave the vision Venus sends
Of supernatural sympathy,
Universal love and hope;
While an abstract insight wakes
Among the glaciers and the rocks
The hermit's carnal ecstasy.

Certainty, fidelity
On the stroke of midnight pass
Like vibrations of a bell
And fashionable madmen raise
Their pedantic boring cry:
Every farthing of the cost,
All the dreaded cards foretell,
Shall be paid, but from this night
Not a whisper, not a thought,
Not a kiss nor look be lost.

Beauty, midnight, vision dies:
Let the winds of dawn that blow
Softly round your dreaming head
Such a day of welcome show
Eye and knocking heart may bless,
Find our mortal world enough;
Noons of dryness find you fed
By the involuntary powers,
Nights of insult let you pass
Watched by every human love.

W. H. Auden

Like a Flame

Rising up
from my weeding
of ripening cane

my eyes
make four
with this man

there ain't
no reason
to laugh

but
I laughing
in confusion

his hands
soft his words
quick his lips
curling as in
prayer

I nod

I like this man

tonight
I go to meet him
like a flame

Grace Nichols

Perspective

What seems to us for us is true.
   The planet has no proper light,
And yet, when Venus is in view,
   No primal star is half so bright.

Coventry Patmore

'She's the blackberry-flower'

She's the blackberry-flower,
the fine raspberry-flower,
she's the plant of best breeding
   your eyes could behold:
she's my darling and dear,
my fresh apple-tree flower,
she is summer in the cold
   between Christmas and Easter.

Anon.
Translated by Thomas Kinsella

Words, for E

The sky is blue, or something. Anyway, it's there.
Your words are hands, stroking me, stroking the sky,
Blue sky, names, people. It's marvellous, I'm king,
And your words are a line of ships. The guns fire.
Blue sky, names, people. I take the salute.

You are beautiful, sometimes. Now.
I feel for words for you. The ship rising, falling,
The horizon, a line rising, falling, behind your hair.
Words rise, spray. I like to think of you as giving
Structure. A gentleness. A constancy.

Tom Leonard

How Do I Love Thee?

I cannot woo thee as the lion his mate,
With proud parade and fierce prestige of presence;
Nor thy fleet fancy may I captivate
With pastoral attitudes in flowery pleasance;
Nor will I kneeling court thee with sedate
And comfortable plans of husbandhood;
Nor file before thee as a candidate . . .
I cannot woo thee as a lover would.

To wrest thy hand from rivals, iron-gloved,
Or cheat them by craft, I am not clever.
But I do love thee even as Shakespeare loved,
Most gently wild, and desperately for ever,
Full-hearted, grave, and manfully in vain,
With thought, high pain, and ever vaster pain.

Wilfred Owen

And You, Helen

And you, Helen, what should I give you?
So many things I would give you
Had I an infinite great store
Offered me and I stood before
To choose. I would give you youth,
All kinds of loveliness and truth,
A clear eye as good as mine,
Lands, waters, flowers, wine,
As many children as your heart
Might wish for, a far better art
Than mine can be, all you have lost
Upon the travelling waters tossed,
Or given to me. If I could choose
Freely in that great treasure-house
Anything from any shelf,
I would give you back yourself,
And power to discriminate
What you want and want it not too late,
Many fair days free from care
And heart to enjoy both foul and fair,
And myself, too, if I could find
Where it lay hidden and it proved kind.

Edward Thomas

The Orange

At lunchtime I bought a huge orange –
The size of it made us all laugh.
I peeled it and shared it with Robert and Dave –
They got quarters and I had a half.

And that orange, it made me so happy,
As ordinary things often do
Just lately. The shopping. A walk in the park.
This is peace and contentment. It's new.

The rest of the day was quite easy.
I did all the jobs on my list
And enjoyed them and had some time over.
I love you. I'm glad I exist.

Wendy Cope

She Walks in Beauty

I

She walks in beauty, like the night
   Of cloudless climes and starry skies;
And all that's best of dark and bright
   Meet in her aspect and her eyes:
Thus mellow'd to that tender light
   Which heaven to gaudy day denies.

II

One shade the more, one ray the less,
   Had half impair'd the nameless grace
Which waves in every raven tress,
   Or softly lightens o'er her face;
Where thoughts serenely sweet express
   How pure, how dear their dwelling place.

III

And on that cheek, and o'er that brow,
   So soft, so calm, yet eloquent,
The smiles that win, the tints that glow,
   But tell of days in goodness spent,
A mind at peace with all below,
   A heart whose love is innocent!

George Gordon, Lord Byron

A Red, Red Rose

My luve is like a red, red rose,
　　That's newly sprung in June:
My luve is like the melodie,
　　That's sweetly play'd in tune.
As fair art thou, my bonie lass,
　　So deep in luve am I,
And I will luve thee still, my dear,
　　Till a' the seas gang dry.
Till a' the seas gang dry, my dear,
　　And the rocks melt wi' the sun!
And I will luve thee still, my dear,
　　While the sands o' life shall run.
And fare-thee-weel, my only luve,
　　And fare-thee-weel a while!
And I will come again, my luve,
　　Tho' it were ten-thousand mile.

Robert Burns

'How do I love thee?'
(Sonnets from the Portuguese, XLIII)

How do I love thee? Let me count the ways.
I love thee to the depth and breadth and height
My soul can reach, when feeling out of sight
For the ends of Being and ideal Grace.
I love thee to the level of everyday's
Most quiet need, by sun and candle-light.
I love thee freely, as men strive for Right:
I love thee purely, as they turn from Praise.
I love thee with the passion put to use
In my old griefs, and with my childhood's faith.
I love thee with a love I seemed to lose
With my lost saints! – I love thee with the breath,
Smiles, tears, of all my life! – and, if God choose,
I shall but love thee better after death.

Elizabeth Barrett Browning

To My Dear and Loving Husband

If ever two were one, then surely we.
If ever man were loved by wife, then thee.
If ever wife was happy in a man,
Compare with me, ye women, if you can.
I prize thy love more than whole mines of gold,
Or all the riches that the east doth hold.
My love is such that rivers cannot quench,
Nor ought but love from thee give recompence.
Thy love is such I can no way repay;
The heavens reward thee manifold, I pray.
Then while we live, in love let's so persever,
That when we live no more we may live ever.

Anne Bradstreet

'April is in my mistress' face'

April is in my mistress' face,
And July in her eyes hath place,
Within her bosom is September,
But in her heart a cold December.

Anon.

Jenny Kiss'd Me

Jenny kiss'd me when we met,
   Jumping from the chair she sat in;
Time, you thief, who love to get
   Sweets into your list, put that in!
Say I'm weary, say I'm sad,
   Say that health and wealth have miss'd me,
Say I'm growing old, but add,
   Jenny kiss'd me.

Leigh Hunt

The Hill

Breathless, we flung us on the windy hill,
   Laughed in the sun, and kissed the lovely grass.
   You said, 'Through glory and ecstasy we pass;
Wind, sun, and earth remain, the birds sing still,
When we are old, are old . . .' 'And when we die
All's over that is ours; and life burns on
Through other lovers, other lips,' said I,
'Heart of my heart, our heaven is now, is won!'

'We are Earth's best, that learnt her lesson here.
   Life is our cry. We have kept the faith!' we said;
   'We shall go down with unreluctant tread
Rose-crowned into the darkness!' . . . Proud we were,
And laughed, that had such brave true things to say.
– And then you suddenly cried, and turned away.

Rupert Brooke

'If thou must love me, let it be for nought'
(Sonnets from the Portuguese, XIV)

If thou must love me, let it be for nought
Except for love's sake only. Do not say
'I love her for her smile . . . her look . . . her way
Of speaking gently, . . . for a trick of thought
That falls in well with mine, and certes brought
A sense of pleasant ease on such a day' –
For these things in themselves, Beloved, may
Be changed, or change for thee, – and love, so wrought,
May be unwrought so. Neither love me for
Thine own dear pity's wiping my cheeks dry,
Since one might well forget to weep who bore
Thy comfort long, and lose thy love thereby.
But love me for love's sake, that evermore
Thou may'st love on through love's eternity,

Elizabeth Barrett Browning

Clock

To keep us in time I've bought this clock
that ticks and strikes in its own time.
I think it is several pieced-together clocks
but no matter, it chimes
on its almost hour and that will do.

You should hear it tick without you.
Like a rocking horse wild for its ghost.
I rest a palm against my chest
and think my heart might chime
as the long hand nears midnight.

Now.   Listen.   For you.   Twelve times . . .

and now the wild horse again, into the night.

Paul Henry

The Ambush

When the face you swore never to forget
Can no longer be remembered,
When a list of regrets is torn up and thrown away
Then the hurt fades,
And you think you've grown strong.
You sit in bars and boast to yourself,
'Never again will I be vulnerable.
It was an aberration to be so open,
A folly, never to be repeated.'
How absurd and fragile such promises.
Hidden from you, crouched
Among the longings you have suppressed
And the desires you imagine tamed,
A sweet pain waits in ambush.
And there will come a day when in a field
Heaven's mouth gapes open,
And on a web the shadow
Of a marigold will smoulder.
Then without warning,
Without a shred of comfort,
Emotions you thought had been put aside
Will flare up within you and bleed you of reason.
The routines which comforted you
And the habits in which you sought refuge
Will bend like sunlight under water,
And go astray.

Once again your body will become a banquet,
Falling heavenwards.
You will loll in spring's sweet avalanche
Without the burden of memory,
And once again
Monstrous love will swallow you.

Brian Patten

You do not

You do not complete me.
You do not make me whole.
Our two does not become the one.
We were not born to be together.
You are not my life.
You are not my Sun.
You are not my Moon at night.
You are not my reason,
My life-blood,
Nor my right.
You are not. You do not.
But you may well be
The chink that bursts the dam.

Philip Ardagh

Here we are again

Sometimes fleeting memories
of you
catch me off-guard
like a scent on the wind
and my mind is filled
with us
and the happiness
of then.

Philip Ardagh

'My life closed twice before its close'

My life closed twice before its close –
It yet remains to see
If Immortality unveil
A third event to me

So huge, so hopeless to conceive
As these that twice befell.
Parting is all we know of heaven,
And all we need of hell.

Emily Dickinson

Goodbye

He said
goodbye.
I shuffled
my feet
and kept a close
watch on my
shoes.
He was talking
I was listening
but he probably
thought I was
not
because I never
even lifted my
head.
I didn't want him
to see
the mess mascara
makes when it
runs.

Carol-Anne Marsh

To Eros

In that I loved you, Love, I worshipped you,
In that I worshipped well, I sacrificed
All of most worth. I bound and burnt and slew
Old peaceful lives; frail flowers; firm friends; and Christ.

I slew all false loves; I slew all true,
That I might nothing love but your truth, Boy.
Fair fame I cast away as bridegrooms do
Their wedding garments in their haste of joy.

But when I fell upon your sandalled feet,
You laughed; you loosed away my lips; you rose.
I heard the singing of your wing's retreat;
Far-flown, I watched you flush the Olympian snows
Beyond my hoping. Starkly I returned
To stare upon the ash of all I burned.

Wilfred Owen

The Faery Earl

Oh, who is this comes ridin',
   Ridin' down the glen?
Is it one of our own Red-Branch Knights
   Or one of the King's men?

With feathers on his helmet,
   And gold upon his shield,
His horse is shod with silver shoes,
   He ridin' through the field!

Oh, this is not a Red-Branch
   Nor one of the King's men,
But this is faery Desmond
   Come ridin' back again.

'O lady of the Castle,
   O lady with gold hair,
O lady with eyes of pity,
   Come down the grey tower stair.

'For I may ask a question,
   And you may answer me,
When the sun is red in the forest,
   And the moon is white on the sea.'

Says she, 'Sir, ask your question,
    And I will answer you;
At sunset or at moonrise
    God send that I speak true!

'I know you by your helmet,
    And by your voice so sweet,
And by your coal-black charger
    With silver on his feet.

'God send you, faery Desmond,
    To come back to your own.'
Says he, 'Your answer, lady,
    Before the sun goes down.

'I'm ridin' ever and ever
    Over the land and sea;
My horse's shoes of silver,
    How long will they last me?'

The lady stood and pondered,
    The salt tear in her eye –
'Oh, would that I had magic
    To make a wise reply.

'Oh, will they wear forever,
  Or will they wear out fast?
Will he ride home this even'
  And stable his horse at last?'

'Sweet lady, quick, your answer!'
  'Now, God, what can I say? –
Those silver shoes will last, sir,
  To ride till Judgement Day.'

He turned, that faery horseman,
  And shook his bridle rein;
'Now, come the Day of Judgement
  Ere I ride home again.'

The sun went down in the forest,
  The moon shone bright as pearl,
The lady lay in the castle,
  And died for the faery Earl.

And ye will see him ridin',
  Ridin' down the glen
Over the seas and the rivers,
  Over the hill and the plain.

Ye'll see the plume on his helmet
   Waftin' among the trees,
And the silver shoes of his charger
   Chasin' the moonlit seas.

He's ridin' ever and ever,
   He'll ride till Judgement Day;
Oh, when that ride is over,
   May he ride home, we pray!

Rosa Mulholland

La Belle Dame sans Merci

O what can ail thee, knight-at-arms,
　　Alone and palely loitering?
The sedge has withered from the lake,
　　And no birds sing.

O what can ail thee, knight-at-arms,
　　So haggard and so woe-begone?
The squirrel's granary is full,
　　And the harvest's done.

I see a lilly on thy brow
　　With anguish moist and fever dew;
And on thy cheek a fading rose
　　Fast withereth too.

I met a lady in the meads,
　　Full beautiful – a faery's child,
Her hair was long, her foot was light,
　　And her eyes were wild.

I made a garland for her head,
　　And bracelets too, and fragrant zone;
She looked at me as she did love,
　　And made sweet moan.

I set her on my pacing steed
   And nothing else saw all day long,
For sideways would she lean, and sing
    A faery's song.

She found me roots of relish sweet,
   And honey wild and manna dew,
And sure in language strange she said –
    'I love thee true'.

She took me to her elfin grot
   And there she wept and sigh'd full sore,
And there I shut her wild, wild eyes
    With kisses four.

And there she lulled me asleep,
   And there I dream'd – Ah! woe betide!
The latest dream I ever dream'd
    On the cold hill side.

I saw pale kings and princes too,
   Pale warriors, death-pale were they all;
Who cried – 'La Belle Dame sans Merci
    Hath thee in thrall!'

I saw their starved lips in the gloam
  With horrid warning gaped wide,
And I awoke and found me here
    On the cold hill's side.

And this is why I sojourn here
  Alone and palely loitering,
Though the sedge is withered from the lake,
    And no birds sing.

John Keats

The Milking Hour

The sun had grown on lessening day
A table large and round
And in the distant vapours grey
Seemed leaning on the ground
When Mary like a lingering flower
Did tenderly agree
To stay beyond her milking hour
And talk awhile with me

We wandered till the distant town
Had silenced nearly dumb
And lessened on the quiet ear
Small as a beetle's hum
She turned her buckets upside-down
And made us each a seat
And there we talked the evening brown
Beneath the rustling wheat

And while she milked her breathing cows
I sat beside the streams
In musing o'er our evening joys
Like one in pleasant dreams
The bats and owls to meet the night
From hollow trees had gone
And e'en the flowers had shut for sleep
And still she lingered on

We mused in rapture side by side
Our wishes seemed as one
We talked of time's retreating tide
And sighed to find it gone
And we had sighed more deeply still
O'er all our pleasures past
If we had known what now we know
That we had met the last

John Clare

'So, we'll go no more a roving'

I

So, we'll go no more a roving
   So late into the night,
Though the heart be still as loving,
   And the moon be still as bright.

II

For the sword outwears its sheath,
   And the soul wears out the breast,
And the heart must pause to breathe,
   And love itself have rest.

III

Though the night was made for loving,
   And the day returns too soon,
Yet we'll go no more a roving
   By the light of the moon.

George Gordon, Lord Byron

The Sick Rose

O Rose thou art sick.
The invisible worm,
That flies in the night
In the howling storm:

Has found out thy bed
Of crimson joy:
And his dark secret love
Does thy life destroy.

William Blake

'I prithee send me back my heart'

I prithee send me back my heart,
   Since I cannot have thine:
For if from yours you will not part,
   Why then shouldst thou have mine?

Yet now I think on't, let it lie:
   To find it were in vain,
For th' hast a thief in either eye
   Would steal it back again.

Why should two hearts in one breast lie,
   And yet not lodge together?
O love, where is thy sympathy,
   If thus our breasts thou sever?

But love is such a mystery,
   I cannot find it out:
For when I think I'm best resolv'd,
   I then am in most doubt.

Then farewell care, and farewell woe,
   I will no longer pine:
For I'll believe I have her heart
   As much as she hath mine.

Sir John Suckling

The Cynic's Only Love Poem

Love comes and goes
And often it has paused,
Then come back to see
The damage it has caused.

Brian Patten

I have lived and I have loved

I have lived and I have loved;
I have waked and I have slept;
I have sung and I have danced;
I have smiled and I have wept;
I have won and wasted treasure;
I have had my fill of pleasure;
And all these things were weariness,
And some of them were dreariness;
And all these things, but two things,
Were emptiness and pain:
And Love – it was the best of them;
And Sleep – worth all the rest of them,
Worth everything but Love to my spirit and my
    brain.
But still my friend, O Slumber,
Till my days complete their number,
For Love shall never, never return to me again!

Charles Mackay

Never Seek to Tell Thy Love

Never seek to tell thy love,
Love that never told can be;
For the gentle wind does move
Silently, invisibly.

I told my love, I told my love.
I told her all my heart,
Trembling, cold, in ghastly fears –
All, she doth depart.

Soon as she was gone from me
A traveller came by
Silently, invisibly –
He took her with a sigh. O, was no deny.

William Blake

Autumn Joke

I thought it was you hurrying behind me,
About to say, 'Stop, nothing's changed!'
But it was only an old sycamore leaf
Blown by the wind, the joker.

Brian Patten

Solitary Observation Brought Back from a Sojourn in Hell

At midnight tears
Run into your ears.

Louise Bogan

Love Lesson

When, unexpectedly, Love returns from its
   disappointments,
And flopping into your arms, lying says,
'This time I have come back to stay,
All other bodies were at best a compromise,'
Then if you are wise
You will choose to believe its lies.

Brian Patten

Sonnet XLII

What lips my lips have kissed, and where, and why,
I have forgotten, and what arms have lain
Under my head till morning; but the rain
Is full of ghosts tonight, that tap and sigh
Upon the glass and listen for reply,
And in my heart there stirs a quiet pain
For unremembered lads that not again
Will turn to me at midnight with a cry.
Thus in the winter stands the lonely tree,
Nor knows what birds have vanished one by one,
Yet knows its boughs more silent than before:
I cannot say what loves have come and gone,
I only know that summer sang in me
A little while, that in me sings no more.

Edna St Vincent Millay

Perhaps –

*(To R.A.L. Died of Wounds in France,
December 23rd, 1915)*

Perhaps some day the sun will shine again,
   And I shall see that still the skies are blue,
And feel once more I do not live in vain,
   Although bereft of You.

Perhaps the golden meadows at my feet
   Will make the sunny hours of Spring seem gay,
And I shall find the white May blossoms sweet,
   Though You have passed away.

Perhaps the summer woods will shimmer bright,
   And crimson roses once again be fair,
And autumn harvest fields a rich delight,
   Although You are not there.

Perhaps some day I shall not shrink in pain
   To see the passing of the dying year,
And listen to the Christmas songs again,
   Although You cannot hear.

But, though kind Time may many joys renew,
　There is one greatest joy I shall not know
Again, because my heart for loss of You
　Was broken, long ago.

Vera Brittain

Sonnet II

Time does not bring relief; you all have lied
Who told me time would ease me of my pain!
I miss him in the weeping of the rain;
I want him at the shrinking of the tide;
The old snows melt from every mountain-side,
And last year's leaves are smoke in every lane;
But last year's bitter loving must remain
Heaped on my heart, and my old thoughts abide!
There are a hundred places where I fear
To go, – so with his memory they brim!
And entering with relief some quiet place
Where never fell his foot or shone his face
I say, 'There is no memory of him here!'
And so stand stricken, so remembering him.

Edna St Vincent Millay

The Lost Love

She dwelt among the untrodden ways
   Beside the springs of Dove;
A Maid whom there were none to praise
   And very few to love:

A violet by a mossy stone
   Half-hidden from the eye!
– Fair as a star, when only one
   Is shining in the sky.

She lived unknown, and few could know
   When Lucy ceased to be;
But she is in her grave, and, oh,
   The difference to me!

William Wordsworth

Remember

Remember me when I am gone away,
  Gone far away into the silent land;
  When you can no more hold me by the hand,
Nor I half turn to go yet turning stay.
Remember me when no more day by day
  You tell me of our future that you plann'd:
  Only remember me; you understand
It will be late to counsel then or pray.
Yet if you should forget me for a while
  And afterwards remember, do not grieve:
  For if the darkness and corruption leave
  A vestige of the thoughts that once I had,
Better by far you should forget and smile
  Than that you should remember and be sad.

Christina Rossetti

Epitaph on the Monument of Sir William Dyer
at Colmworth, 1641

My dearest dust, could not thy hasty day
Afford thy drowsy patience leave to stay
One hour longer: so that we might either
Sit up, or gone to bed together?
But since thy finished labour hath possessed
Thy weary limbs with early rest,
Enjoy it sweetly: and thy widow bride
Shall soon repose her by thy slumbering side.
Whose business, now, is only to prepare
My nightly dress, and call to prayer:
Mine eyes wax heavy and the day grows old,
The dew falls thick, my blood grows cold.
Draw, draw the closed curtains: and make room:
My dear, my dearest dust; I come, I come.

Lady Catherine Dyer

Index of First Lines

117

I hid my love when young while I 11
I ne'er was struck before that hour 4
I prithee send me back my heart 102
I thought it was you hurrying behind me 106
I will make you brooches and toys for your delight 38
I wish I could remember the first day 52
If ever two were one, then surely we 78
If thou must love me, let it be for nought 82
In my sky at twilight you are like a cloud 1
In that I loved you, Love, I worshipped you 90
In the licorice fields at Pontefract 36
Jenny kiss'd me when we met 80
Lay your sleeping head, my love 65
Let me not to the marriage of true minds 53
Looking up at the stars, I know quite well 43
Love comes and goes 103
Love is a circle that doth restless move 9
Love is like the wild rose briar 40
Lying asleep between the strokes of night 7
My dearest dust, could not thy hasty day 115
My heart has made its mind up 57
My heart is like a singing bird 54
My life closed twice before its close 88
My luve is like a red, red rose 76
My true love hath my heart, and I have his 59
My woman says she wants no other lover 62
Never seek to tell thy love 105
O lurcher-loving collier, black as night 2
O mighty goddess, day star after night 10

Index of Titles

Index of Poets

Acknowledgements

The publisher wishes to thank the following for permission to use copyright material:

Philip Ardagh, 'Always', 'You do not' and 'Here we are again' by permission of the author; W. H. Auden, 'O lurcher-loving collier, black as night', 'The More Loving One' and 'Lullaby' from *Collected Poems* by permission of Faber and Faber Ltd; John Betjeman, 'The Licorice Fields at Pontefract' from *Collected Poems* by permission of John Murray Ltd; Louise Bogan, 'Solitary Observation Brought Back from a Sojourn in Hell' from *The Blue Estuaries* by Louise Bogan. Copyright © 1968 by Louise Bogan. Copyright renewed 1996 by Ruth Limmer. Reprinted by permission of Farrar, Straus and Giroux, LLC; Vera Brittain, 'Perhaps –' by permission of Mark Bostridge and Timothy Brittain-Catlin, Literary Executors for the Estate of Vera Brittain, 1970; Wendy Cope, 'Valentine' and 'The Orange' from *Serious Concerns* by permission of Faber and Faber Ltd; Frances Cornford, 'The Avenue' by permission of the author's estate; E. E. Cummings, 'i carry your heart with me' from *Complete Poems 1904–1962* by E. E. Cummings, edited by George J. Firmage, by permission of W. W. Norton & Company. Copyright © 1991 by the Trustees for the E. E. Cummings Trust and George James Firmage; Carol Ann Duffy, 'Words, Wide Night' from *The Other Country* by permission of Anvil Press; Robert Graves, 'She tells her love while half asleep' from *Complete Poems in One Volume* by permission of Carcanet Press Limited; Paul Henry, 'The Drunk and the Night Runner', 'Violin Tide' and 'Clock' by permission of the author; Jenny Joseph, 'The sun has burst the sky', first published in *All the Things I See* by Macmillan Children's Books, by permission of the author; Tom Leonard, 'Words, for E' from *Poems* published by E & T O'Brien, Dublin 1973. By permission of the author; Carol-Anne Marsh, 'Goodbye' from *Let's Hurry Up and Get This Relationship Over, So I Can Get on with Decorating the Hallway: Book of Love Poetry* published by Bristol Broadsides; Edna St Vincent Millay, Sonnet XLII ('What my lips have kissed') and Sonnet II ('Time does not bring relief') by permission of A. M. Heath & Co. Ltd. Author's Agents; Pablo Neruda, Poem XVI 'In My Sky at Twilight' from *Twenty Love Poems* – translation by permission of Jonathan Cape Ltd – and Poem XVII 'I Do Not Love You' from *100 Love Sonnets* – translation by permission of the University of Texas Press – both poems by permission of the Fundacion Pablo Neruda; Grace Nichols, 'Like a Flame' by permission of Curtis Brown Ltd on behalf of the author; Gareth Owen, 'Schoolgirl on a Train' and 'Envelopes and Letters' by permission of the author; Brian Patten, 'Her Song', 'The Ambush', 'The Cynic's Only Love Poem', 'Autumn Joke' and 'Love Lesson' from *Collected Love Poems*, Harper Perennial, by permission of Rogers, Coleridge and White, Literary Agents; Roger Stevens, 'Our Love Is Loud' by permission of the author.

Every effort has been made to trace the copyright holders, but if any have been inadvertently overlooked the publisher will be pleased to make the necessary arrangement at the first opportunity.

EVERMORE

THE IMMORTALS

Alyson Noël

SOMETIMES LOVE IS ETERNAL.
FOR GOOD . . . FOR EVIL . . .
FOREVER

Sixteen-year-old Ever Bloom is the sole survivor of a car accident that killed her family. Exiled to sunny California, Ever is haunted by her little sister and by the ability to see people's auras, hear their thoughts and know their entire life story by touching them. She wants to hide from the world, but when a stunningly handsome new guy arrives at school, she can't seem to keep away. Falling in love with Damen is dangerous – he's not what he seems. But if Damen is her destiny, how can Ever walk away?

KISSED
BY AN
ANGEL

Elizabeth Chandler

IF THE LOVE OF YOUR LIFE DIED,
WHAT WOULD YOU MISS THE MOST?

HIS VOICE?

HIS TOUCH?

HIS HEART BEATING AGAINST
YOURS?

When Ivy's boyfriend Tristan dies, she's deso-
late without him, until she discovers Tristan
hasn't abandoned her – he's her guardian
angel, watching over her, close enough to
hear, to see, to touch.

But Ivy's life is in danger. If Tristan rescues
her, his mission on earth will be over and he'll
have to leave her behind. Will Ivy lose Tristan
forever?

A selected list of titles available from Macmillan Children's Books

The prices shown below are correct at the time of going to press. However, Macmillan Publishers reserves the right to show new retail prices on covers, which may differ from those previously advertised.

Alyson Noël

| The Immortals: Evermore | 978-0-330-51285-5 | £6.99 |
| The Immortals: Blue Moon | 978-0-330-51286-2 | £6.99 |

Elizabeth Chandler

| Kissed by an Angel | 978-0-330-51149-0 | £6.99 |

Chosen by Roger McGough

| Sensational! Poems inspired by the five senses | 978-0-330-41344-2 | £6.99 |

All Pan Macmillan titles can be ordered from our website, www.panmacmillan.com, or from your local bookshop and are also available by post from:

Bookpost, PO Box 29, Douglas, Isle of Man IM99 1BQ

Credit cards accepted. For details:
Telephone: 01624 677237
Fax: 01624 670923
Email: bookshop@enterprise.net
www.bookpost.co.uk

Free postage and packing in the United Kingdom